GARFIELD

JiM DAVıS

ℛ
RAVETTE PUBLISHING

First published in 2002 by
Ravette Publishing Limited, Unit 3, Tristar Centre,
Star Road, Partridge Green, West Sussex RH13 8RA

Printed in Malta by Gutenberg Press

ISBN: 1 84161 147 6

WELCOME TO MY
LITTLE BOOK OF LOVE 'N' STUFF!

It's impossible to give a hug
without getting one back.

Irresistible ...
just like you!

Psst.
Can I interest you in
a little romance?

I'm yours. You're mine. Everyone else will have to settle for second best.

The things we do for love.

I love you in the springtime,
I love you in the fall.

In fact, apart from myself,
I love you most of all!

You bring out
the hugs in me!

You and I
will be friends forever –
provided you bath regularly,
share your food
and don't get on my nerves!

I love you
for what you are ...
What are you?

Women don't appreciate
us strong silent types.

I've been waiting to hear those three little words from you that would make me so very happy —
"I'm very rich!"

All of my personalities
love you!

Home is where
they understand you.

Love you beary much!

We make beautiful music
together.

You're so attractive,
you oughta be in pictures!

Life is more fun if you get
a few licks now and then.

Love will keep us
together.

Human love ...
it's so glandular!

Christmas Spirit ...
it's not the giving,
it's not the receiving –
it's the loving!

I've got the time ...
if you've got the lips!

It's nice to be liked
just the way you are!

Some of my best friends
are books!

Beneath this cool exterior
is a powder of passion!

Without you,
life is one big Monday!

I love my teddy bear

I break for friends.

When I kiss 'em,
they stay kissed!

To know me is to love me.

I thought of you today!

The sky's the limit for us!

Life's simple pleasures
are the best.

Friends like you
are hard to find.

Ahoy, mate.
Wish you were here.

'Tis the season to be kissin'!

I shoot to thrill.

There are no hugs
like bear hugs!

Prisoners have more dates
than I do!

Your friendship keeps
lifting me higher.

If you don't love yourself,
who will?!

Ready when you are ...

Everyone needs a loyal, understanding, considerate friend ... but fun friends like you are essential, too!

It's unnatural
to be near someone you love
and not hold them
now and again.

I wouldn't sell our friendship
for a million dollars –
but five million and we'll talk!

Rub-a-dub-dub,
fun in the tub!

Cute enough for ya?

Friends are forever.